THE BEST ME I CAN BE™

I Can Make Good Choices!

by David Parker
Illustrated by Jill Dubin

SCHOLASTIC INC.
New York Toronto London Auckland Sydney
Mexico City New Delhi Hong Kong Buenos Aires

To my nieces and nephews, I pray that you will.
— D.P.

To Henry and Nina, with love.
— J.D.

ISBN 0-439-69360-8

Text copyright © 2004 by David Parker
Illustrations copyright © 2004 by Jill Dubin
All rights reserved. Published by Scholastic Inc.
SCHOLASTIC, THE BEST ME I CAN BE™ Readers, and associated logos are trademarks and/or registered trademarks of Scholastic Inc.

12 11   7 8 9/0

Printed in the U.S.A.
First printing, October 2004

Which shirt should I wear when it is cold outside?

Do I cross the street in the middle or at the corner?

I stop. . . . I think. . . . I can make a good choice!

Do I look at my classmate's paper
and copy the answer?

Should I tell the truth even if it is hard to do?

Should I scream and shout or talk about how I am feeling inside?

I stop. . . . I think. . . . I can make a good choice!

Should I take something that doesn't belong to me
even if I really like it?

Should I walk or run on the stairs?

Should I say something nice or something mean to my classmates?

I stop. . . . I think. . . . I can make a good choice!

Should I do something that I know isn't right because my friend tells me to?

Should I go with someone I do not know?

I stop. . . . I think. . . . I can make a good choice!
What are two good choices you made today?